1 Short Vowel Review

Five Short Vowel Sounds

...will review short vowels to prepare for learning long vowels in this book.

■ Color the pictures in this scene, using the key below.
(Say) the words out loud as you go.

short a = orange ▶   short e = yellow ▶   short i = pink ▶

short o = black ▶   short u = brown ▶

pig

mud

dog

cat

hen

bug

tin

a b c d e f g h i j k l m n o p q r s t u v w x y z

■ Color the pictures in this scene, using the key below.
(Say) the words out loud as you go.

short a = black ▶ short e = blue ▶ short i = brown ▶
short o = red ▶ short u = yellow ▶

a b c d e f g h i j k l m n o p q r s t u v w x y z

Short Vowel Review

The Short "a" and Short "e" Sounds

Name

Date

/　　/

To parents/guardians: Throughout this book, it is important that you encourage your child to say each word out loud. This will help your child learn the relationships between letters and sounds.

■ (Say) the word represented by the picture out loud. Then write in the missing letter: a or e.

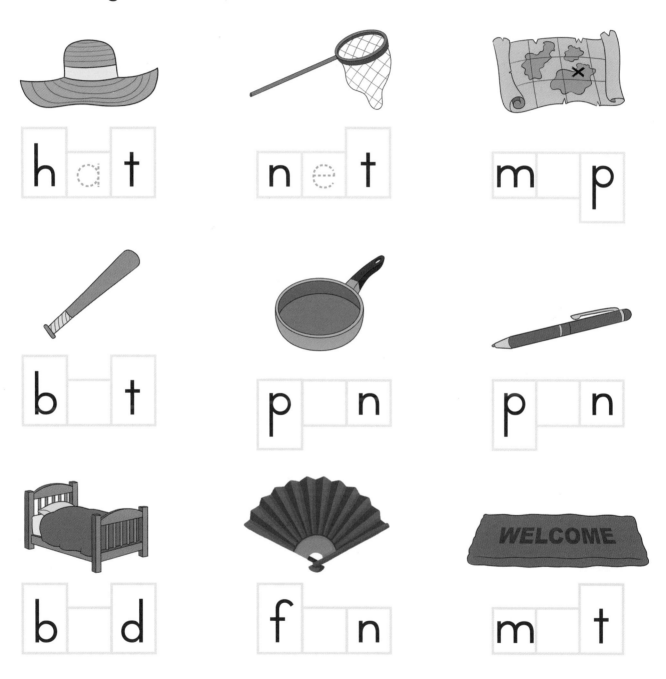

h [a] t

n [e] t

m　p

b　t

p　n

p　n

b　d

f　n

m　t

| a | b | c | d | e | f | g | h | i | j | k | l | m | n | o | p | q | r | s | t | u | v | w | x | y | z |

To parents/guardians: If your child has trouble identifying the word shown in the picture, you can say the word aloud. Have your child listen and repeat after you.

■ (Say) the word represented by the picture out loud. Then write in the missing letter: a or e.

b   g   y   l   l   c   t

r   d   s   n   d   l   g

l   s   t   h   n   v   n

a b c d e f g h i j k l m n o p q r s t u v w x y z

Short Vowel Review

The Short "i", "o", and "u" Sounds

Name _____ Date ___ / ___ / ___

To parents/guardians: If your child has trouble identifying the word shown in the picture, you can say the word aloud. Have your child listen and repeat after you.

■ (Say) the word represented by the picture out loud. Then write in the missing letter: i, o, or u.

t i n   m u g   l o g

t p   m p   n t

s n   p g   r p

a b c d e f g h i j k l m n o p q r s t u v w x y z

■ ⟨Say⟩ the word represented by the picture out loud. Then write in the missing letter: i, o, or u.

h   g   t   p   p   p

f   n   g   m   c   p

h   t   l   p   s   c   p

a b c d e f g h **i** j k l m n **o** p q r s t **u** v w x y z

4 Consonant Sounds Review

Name

Date

/   /

To parents/guardians: In this section, your child will review consonant letter sounds. Make sure your child says each word out loud correctly to reinforce the letter sounds.

■ (Say) the word represented by the picture out loud. Then circle the beginning letter of the word.

■ (Say) the word represented by the picture out loud. Then write in the missing letter.

f o r k   o l d   a m p

o l l   o o k   r e e n

i n g   e t   e a r t

a b c d e f g h i j k l m n o p q r s t u v w x y z

5 Consonant Sounds Review

Name

Date / /

■ Say the word represented by the picture out loud. Then circle the beginning letter or letters of the word.

n v

h t

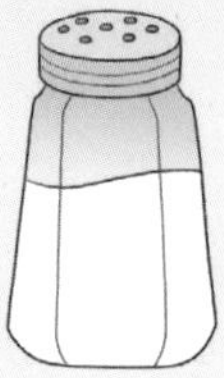
r s

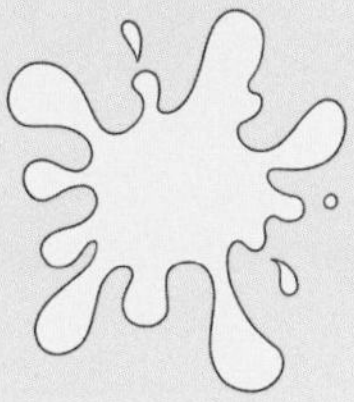
k y

w x

qu z

r t

c v

j p

z j

a	b	c	d	e	f	g	h	i	j	k	l	m	n	o	p	q	r	s	t	u	v	w	x	y	z

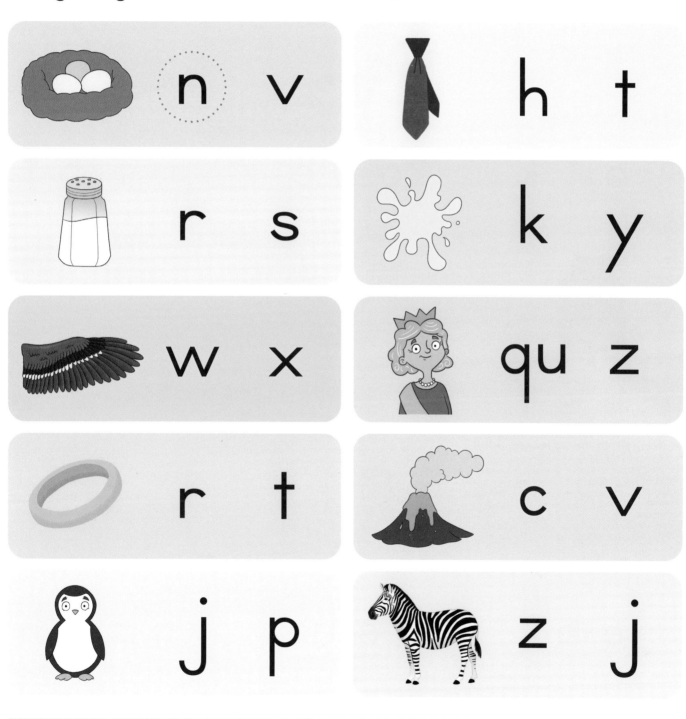

■ (Say) the word represented by the picture out loud. Then write in the missing letter or letters.

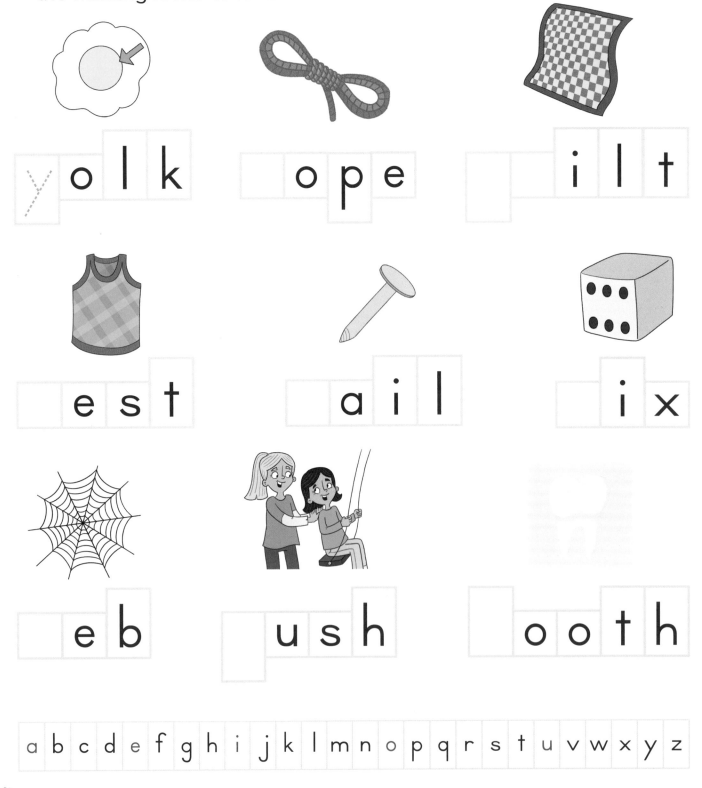

y o l k

o p e

i l t

e s t

a i l

i x

e b

u s h

o o t h

a b c d e f g h i j k l m n o p q r s t u v w x y z

6 Soft "c" and "g"
The Soft "c" Sound

Name

Date

/ /

To parents/guardians: The letter *c* can make a hard "c" sound, as in "card," and a soft "c" sound, as in the initial sound in "circle." Here your child will focus on words with the soft "c" sound.

■ (Say) the word represented by the picture out loud. Then circle the letter that makes the soft "c" sound at the beginning of the word.

city   celery   cent

cereal   circle

circus   cell phone

| a | b | c | d | e | f | g | h | i | j | k | l | m | n | o | p | q | r | s | t | u | v | w | x | y | z |

To parents/guardians: It is helpful to have your child say each word out loud as they trace the path.

■ Draw a line along the path from the dot (●) to the star (★).
Each time you pass an image, (say) the word out loud.

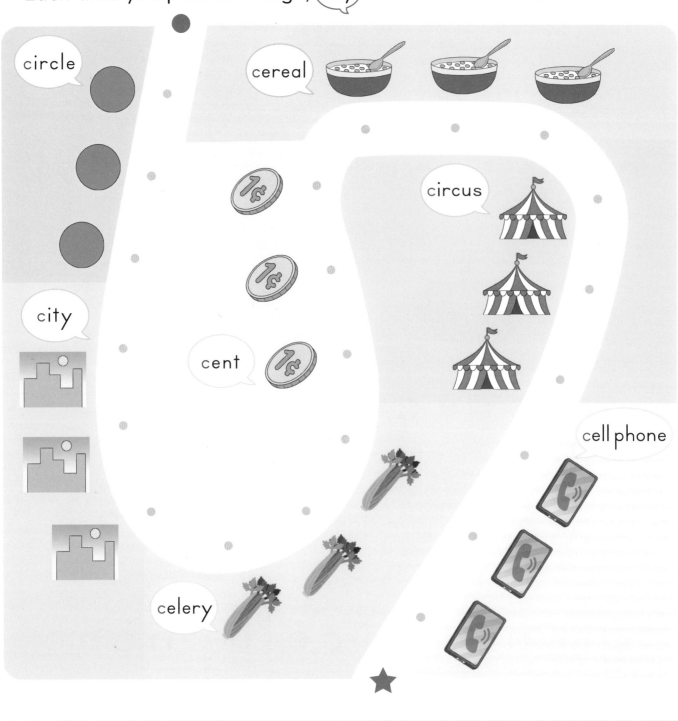

a b c d e f g h i j k l m n o p q r s t u v w x y z

Soft "c" and "g"
The Soft "g" Sound

Name

Date

/ /

To parents/guardians: The letter *g* can make a hard "g" sound, as in "goat," and a soft "g" sound, as in "gem." Here your child will focus on words with the soft "g" sound.

■ (Say) the word represented by the picture out loud. Then circle the letter that makes the soft "g" sound at the beginning of the word.

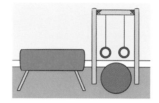

g e m

g y m

g e l

g i r a f f e

g i a n t

g y m n a s t

g i n g e r

| a | b | c | d | e | f | g | h | i | j | k | l | m | n | o | p | q | r | s | t | u | v | w | x | y | z |

■ Draw a line along the path from the dot (●) to the star (★).
Each time you pass an image, (say) the word out loud.

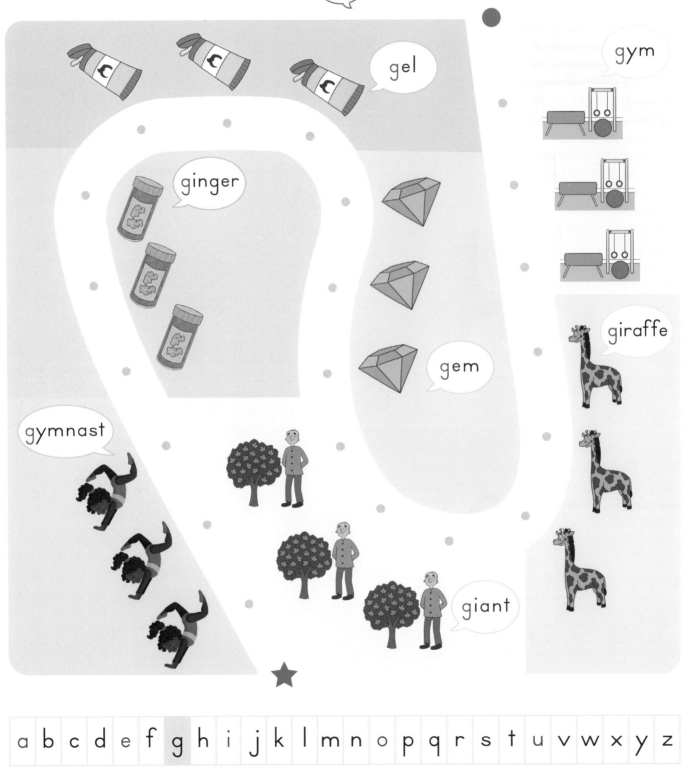

Soft "c" and "g" Review

Name

Date

/ /

To parents/guardians: On this page, your child will practice distinguishing between soft "c" and hard "c" sounds.

■ Say the words represented by the pictures out loud. Two words in each row begin with the soft "c" sound. Circle them.

city

cent

cat

celery

corn

cereal

call

circle

circus

a b c d e f g h i j k l m n o p q r s t u v w x y z

■ (Say) the words represented by the pictures out loud. Two words in each row begin with the soft "g" sound. Circle them.

gym   girl   giraffe

gold   gem   ginger

gel   gymnast   gift

a b c d e f g h i j k l m n o p q r s t u v w x y z

Long Vowel Sounds

Introducing the Long "a" Sound

Name

Date

/   /

To parents/guardians: This is the beginning of the section in which your child will learn long vowel sounds. It is important to note that long vowels say their name. For example, long "a" makes the "a" sound in "pay" but not in "cat."

■ (Say) the word represented by the picture out loud. Then circle the first vowel (a) in the word.

m (a) n e

p a y

c a g e

r a i n

c a n e

g a t e

c a k e

m a i l

h a y

a b c d e f g h i j k l m n o p q r s t u v w x y z

■ Draw a line along the path from the dot (●) to the star (★). Each time you pass an image, (say) the word out loud.

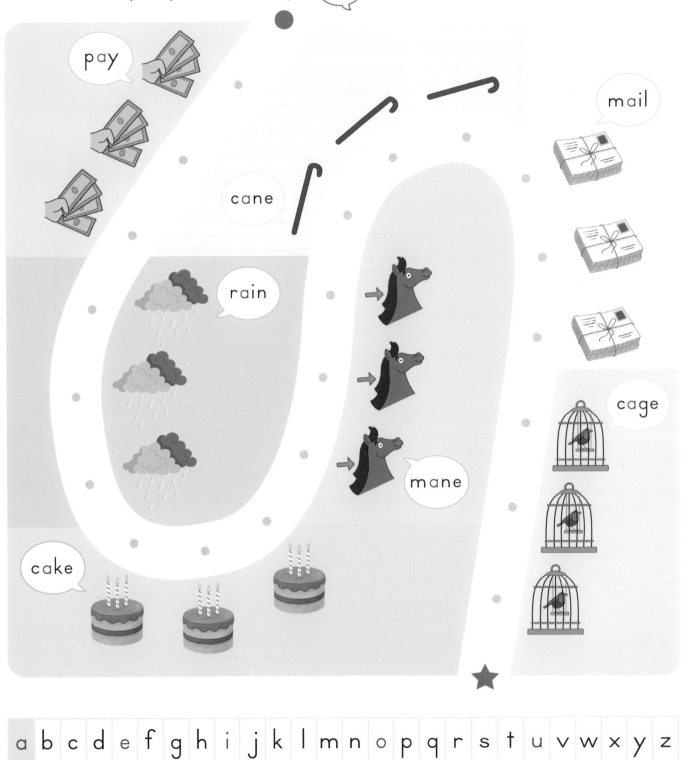

a b c d e f g h i j k l m n o p q r s t u v w x y z

Long Vowel Sounds

Recognizing the Long "a" Sound

Name

Date

/ /

To parents/guardians: If your child has trouble circling the right words, have them say all the words out loud again. Encourage them to listen for the two words in each row that rhyme.

■ Say the words represented by the pictures out loud. Two words in each row have the long "a" sound. Circle them.

rain   mail   bee

pot   mane   gate

cake   vine   hay

a	b	c	d	e	f	g	h	i	j	k	l	m	n	o	p	q	r	s	t	u	v	w	x	y	z

To parents/guardians: This activity introduces your child to the general idea that words with long vowels contain a "silent" vowel. At this point, it is not necessary for your child to memorize the various vowel combinations and spelling rules for long vowel words.

■ (Say) the word represented by the picture out loud. Then write in the missing letter a. Trace the other vowel.

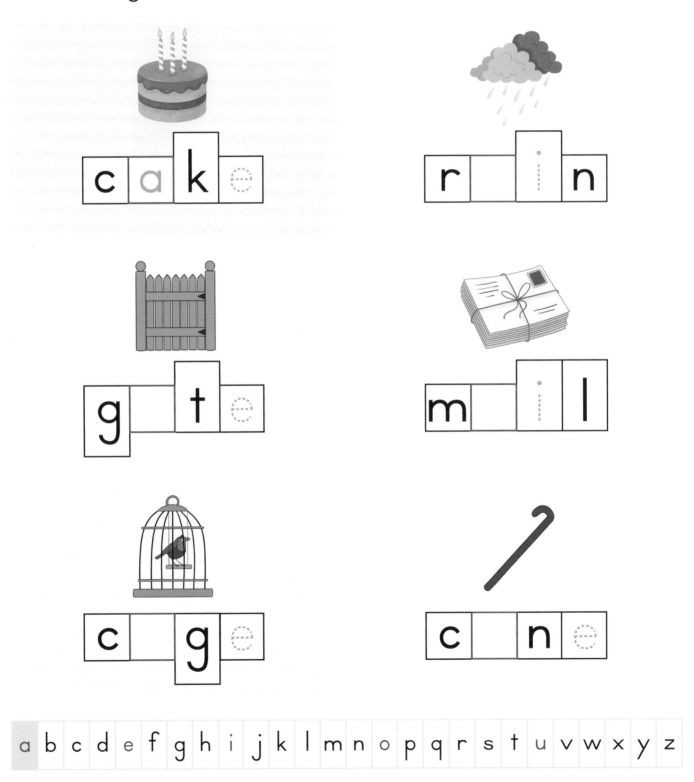

Long Vowel Sounds
Introducing the Long "e" Sound

To parents/guardians: This page introduces your child to the long "e" sound. Make sure your child says each word out loud as they complete the activity. This will help them identify the long "e" sound.

■ **Say** the word represented by the picture out loud. Then circle the first vowel (e) in the word.

t e a

s e e

p e a s

f e e t

b e e

b e a n

t e a m

t r e e

g r e e n

a b c d e f g h i j k l m n o p q r s t u v w x y z

■ Draw a line along the path from the dot (●) to the star (★).
Each time you pass an image, (say) the word out loud.

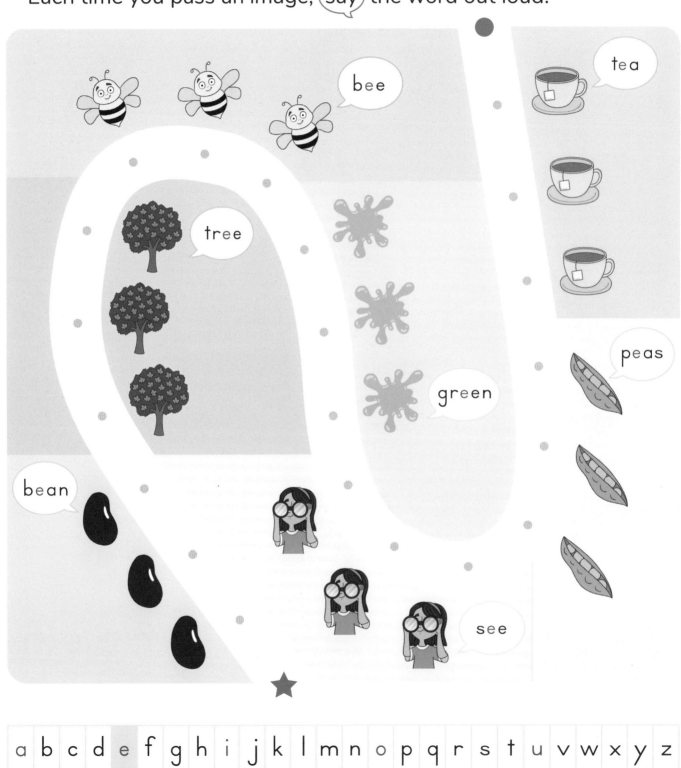

| a | b | c | d | e | f | g | h | i | j | k | l | m | n | o | p | q | r | s | t | u | v | w | x | y | z |

12 Long Vowel Sounds
Recognizing the Long "e" Sound

To parents/guardians: To support your child learning with ease and without frustration, please make sure that they complete the pages of this workbook in order.

■ (Say) the words represented by the pictures out loud. Two words in each row have the long "e" sound. Circle them.

tea   peas   map

pig   bee   bean

team   tin   green

a b c d e f g h i j k l m n o p q r s t u v w x y z

To parents/guardians: This activity introduces your child to the general idea that words with long vowels often contain a "silent" vowel. At this point, it is not necessary for your child to learn the various vowel combinations and spelling rules for long vowel words.

■ (Say) the word represented by the picture out loud. Then write in the missing letter e. Trace the other vowel.

Long Vowel Sounds
Introducing the Long "i" Sound

Name   Date

_____/_____/_____

To parents/guardians: This page introduces your child to the long "i" sound. Make sure your child says each word out loud as they complete the activity. This will help them identify the long "i" sound.

■ Say the word represented by the picture out loud. Then circle the first vowel (i) in the word.

f (i) v e

b i k e

k i t e

r i d e

i c e

h i k e

t i e

s l i d e

t i m e

a b c d e f g h i j k l m n o p q r s t u v w x y z

■ Draw a line along the path from the dot (●) to the star (★).
Each time you pass an image, say the word out loud.

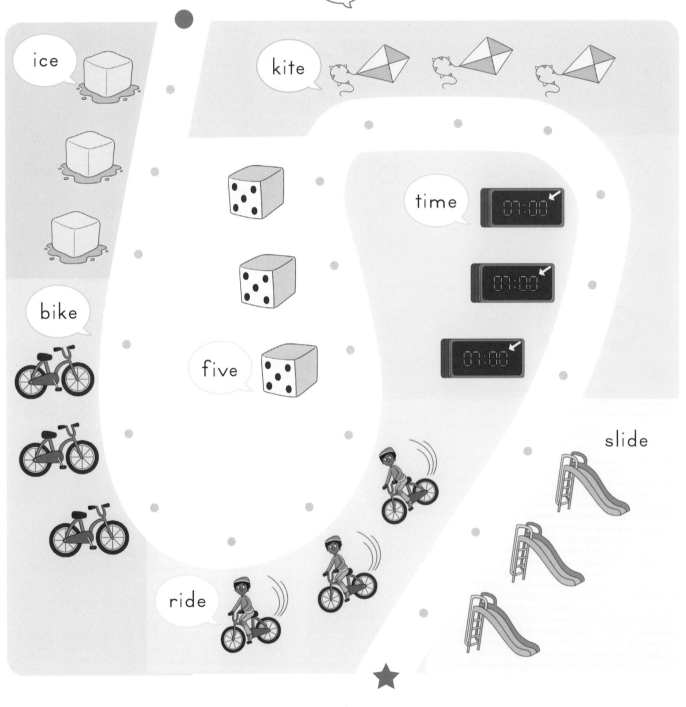

a b c d e f g h i j k l m n o p q r s t u v w x y z

14 Long Vowel Sounds
Recognizing the Long "i" Sound

■ (Say) the words represented by the pictures out loud. Two words in each row have the long "i" sound. Circle them.

hike   ice   pan

five   den   tie

hot   stripe   slide

a b c d e f g h i j k l m n o p q r s t u v w x y z

■ (Say) the word represented by the picture out loud. Then write in the missing letter i. Trace the other vowel.

r i d e

t _ e

h _ k e

s l _ d e

b _ k e

_ c e

a b c d e f g h i j k l m n o p q r s t u v w x y z

15 Long Vowel Sounds

Reviewing the Long "a", "e", and "i" Sounds

To parents/guardians: On this page, your child will review long vowel sounds. It is helpful to have your child say the word represented by each picture out loud to distinguish between the long vowel sounds.

Name _____   Date ___/___/___

■ Trace each path from dot (●) to star (★) by following the words with the same long vowel sound. (Say) each word as you go.

long "a"   long "e"   long "i"

long "e"   long "i"   long "a"

a b c d e f g h i j k l m n o p q r s t u v w x y z

■ (Say) the word represented by the picture out loud. Then write in the missing letter.

p _ y   m i _ l   c _ n e

f _ e t   b _ a n   t r _ e

h _ k e   t _ m e   _ c e

a b c d e f g h i j k l m n o p q r s t u v w x y z

16 Long Vowel Sounds
Introducing the Long "o" Sound

To parents/guardians: This page introduces your child to the long "o" sound. Make sure your child says each word out loud as they complete the activity. This will help them identify the long "o" sound.

■ Say the word represented by the picture out loud. Then circle the first vowel (o) in the word.

c o a t

b o n e

g o a t

r o s e

b o a t

h o m e

h o l e

n o s e

s t o n e

a b c d e f g h i j k l m n o p q r s t u v w x y z

■ Draw a line along the path from the dot (●) to the star (★).
Each time you pass an image, (say) the word out loud.

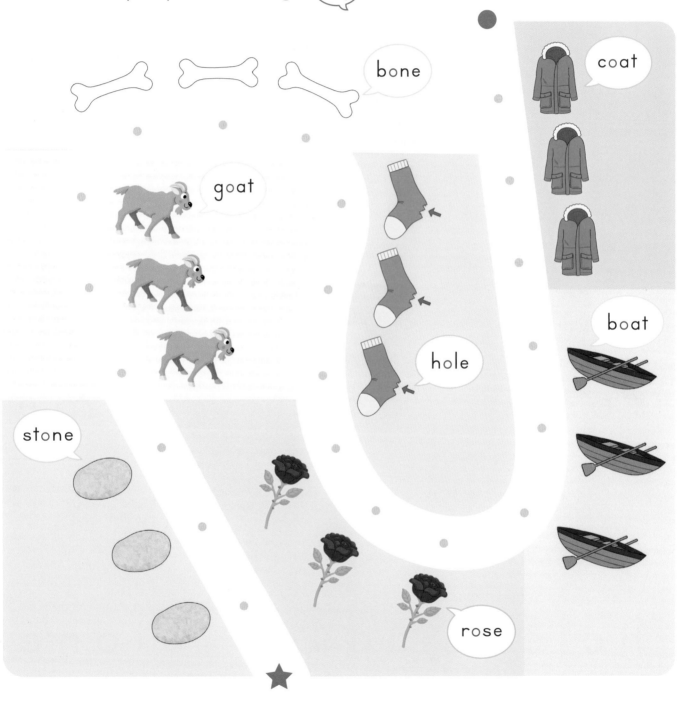

a b c d e f g h i j k l m n o p q r s t u v w x y z

17 Long Vowel Sounds

Recognizing the Long "o" Sound

To parents/guardians: If your child has trouble circling the right words, have them say all the words out loud again. Encourage them to listen for the two words in each row that rhyme.

Name

Date   /   /

■ Say the words represented by the pictures out loud. Two words in each row have the long "o" sound. Circle them.

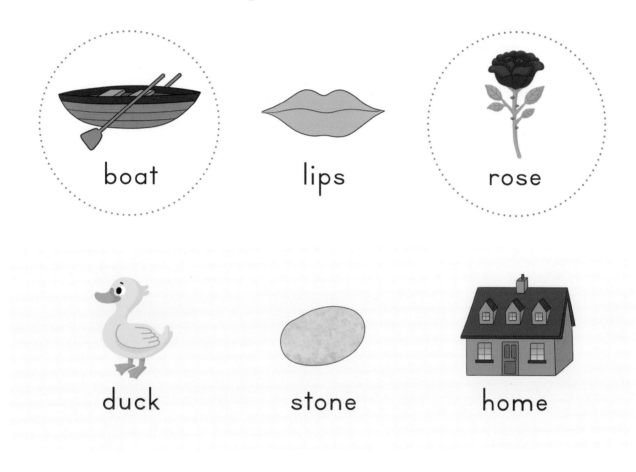

boat   lips   rose

duck   stone   home

hole   nose   hug

a b c d e f g h i j k l m n o p q r s t u v w x y z

■ (Say) the word represented by the picture out loud. Then write in the missing letter o. Trace the other vowel.

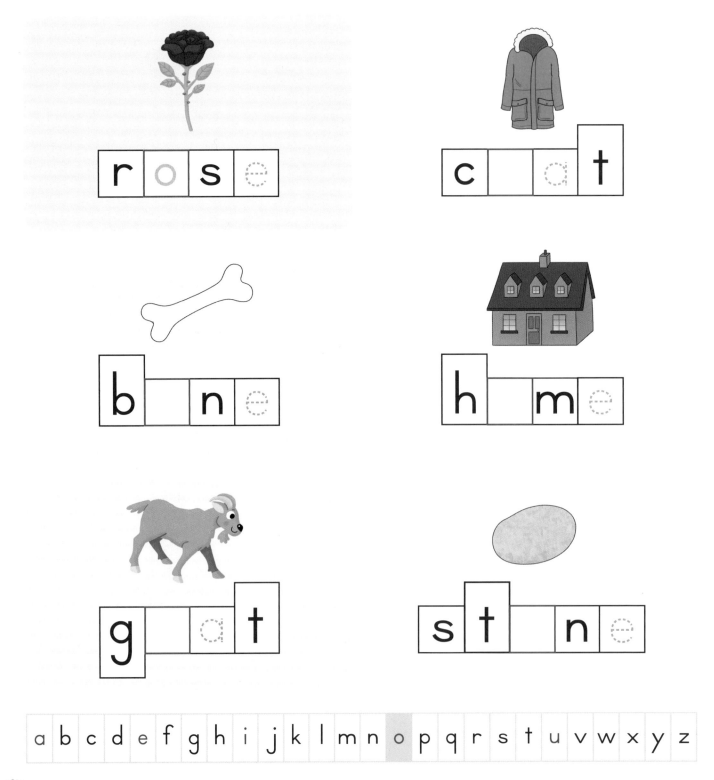

| r | o | s | e |

c [ ] a t

b [ ] n e

h [ ] m e

g [ ] a t

s t [ ] n e

| a | b | c | d | e | f | g | h | i | j | k | l | m | n | o | p | q | r | s | t | u | v | w | x | y | z |

Long Vowel Sounds

Introducing the Long "u" Sound

To parents/guardians: This page introduces your child to the long "u" sound. Make sure your child says each word out loud as they complete the activity. This will help them identify the long "u" sound.

■ (Say) the word represented by the picture out loud. Then circle the first vowel (u) in the word.

c (u) b e

m u l e

t u b e

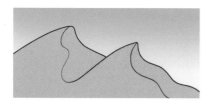

d u n e

t u n e

g l u e

b l u e

c l u e

f l u t e

a b c d e f g h i j k l m n o p q r s t u v w x y z

■ Draw a line along the path from the dot (●) to the star (★).
Each time you pass an image, (say) the word out loud.

a b c d e f g h i j k l m n o p q r s t u v w x y z

Long Vowel Sounds

Recognizing the Long "u" Sound

Name

Date

/   /

■ Say the words represented by the pictures out loud. Two words in each row have the long "u" sound. Circle them.

glue

mop

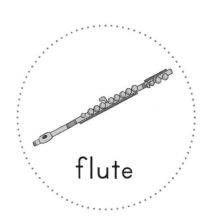

flute

blue

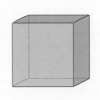

cube

rip

red

dune

tune

a	b	c	d	e	f	g	h	i	j	k	l	m	n	o	p	q	r	s	t	u	v	w	x	y	z

■ (Say) the word represented by the picture out loud. Then write in the missing letter u. Trace the other vowel.

a b c d e f g h i j k l m n o p q r s t u v w x y z

20 Long Vowel Sounds

Reviewing the Long "o" and "u" Sounds

Name

Date

/   /

To parents/guardians: Here your child will review long vowel sounds "o" and "u."

■ Trace each path from dot (●) to star (★) by following the words with the same long vowel sound. (Say) each word as you go.

long "o"   ●

long "u"   ●

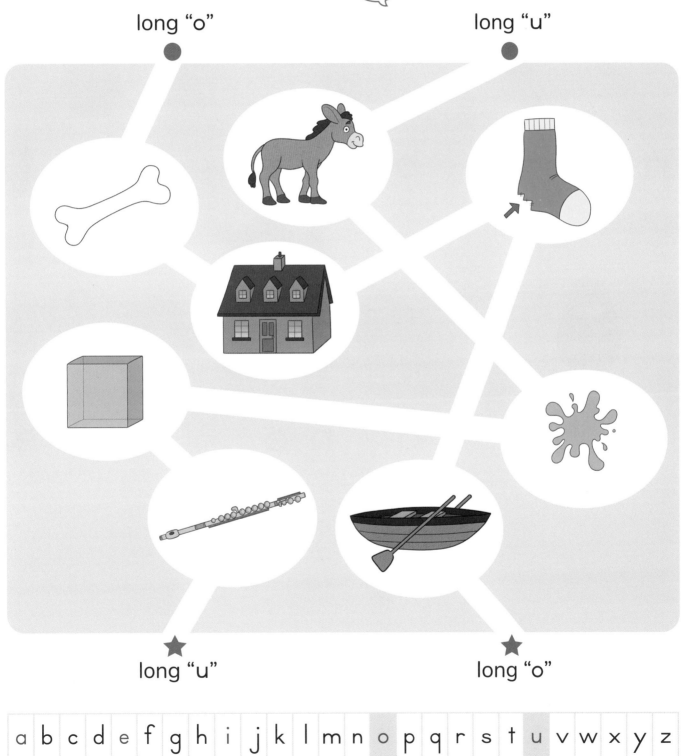

★ long "u"

★ long "o"

| a | b | c | d | e | f | g | h | i | j | k | l | m | n | o | p | q | r | s | t | u | v | w | x | y | z |

■ (Say) the word represented by the picture out loud. Then write in
   the missing letter.

n　s　e　　　　b　n　e　　　　c　a　t

t　b　e　　　　d　n　e　　　　c　l　e

a b c d e f g h i j k l m n o p q r s t u v w x y z

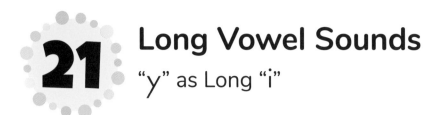

21 Long Vowel Sounds

"y" as Long "i"

To parents/guardians: In this section, your child will learn sounds the letter *y* makes when used as a vowel. *Y* can make the long "i" sound or the long "e" sound, often at the end of a word. When a word does not have a vowel present, but has a *y*, the *y* usually serves as a vowel.

Name _____   Date _____ / _____ / _____

■ (Say) the word represented by the picture out loud. Then circle the letter that makes the long "i" sound.

cry   fry   sky

fly   dry

spy   python

a b c d e f g h i j k l m n o p q r s t u v w x **y** z

■ Draw a line along the path from the dot (●) to the star (★).
Each time you pass an image, (say) the word out loud.

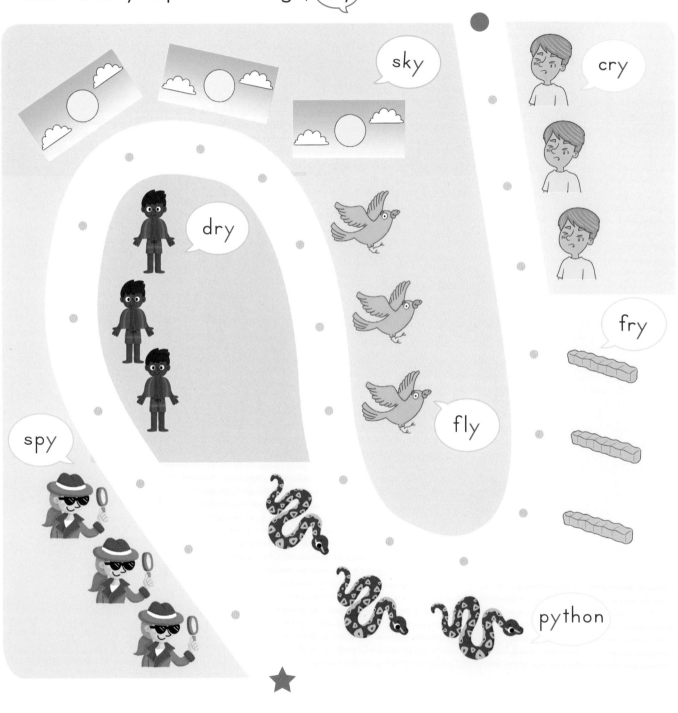

a b c d e f g h i j k l m n o p q r s t u v w x y z

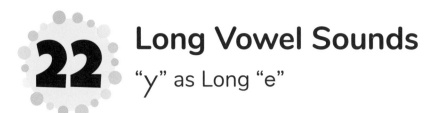
Name

Date
/ /

To parents/guardians: Here your child will practice *y* as long "e" at the end of each word. Remind your child that *y* can be a consonant or a vowel.

■ (Say) the word represented by the picture out loud. Then circle the letter that makes the long "e" sound.

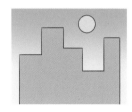

b a b **(y)**   c i t y   c a n d y

p e n n y   p u p p y

f l u f f y   c h e r r y

| a | b | c | d | e | f | g | h | i | j | k | l | m | n | o | p | q | r | s | t | u | v | w | x | y | z |

■ Draw a line along the path from the dot (●) to the star (★).
Each time you pass an image, (say) the word out loud.

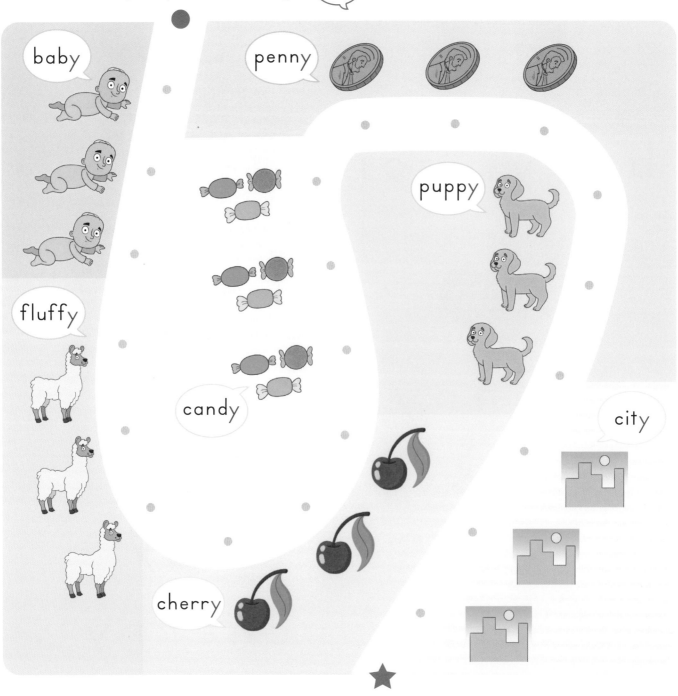

a b c d e f g h i j k l m n o p q r s t u v w x y z

Long Vowel Sounds

23

Comparing Long and Short "a" and "e"

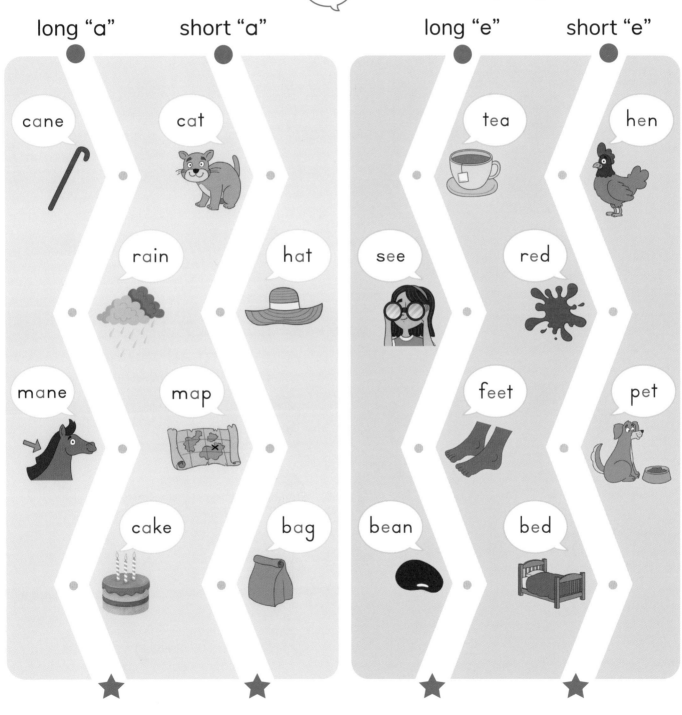

Name

Date

/ /

To parents/guardians: This section will review long and short vowel sounds. It is very important to have your child say each word out loud as they trace the paths. This will help them distinguish between the different sounds long and short vowels make.

■ Trace each path from dot (●) to star (★) by following the words with the same vowel sound. Say each word as you go.

long "a"   short "a"   long "e"   short "e"

cane   cat   tea   hen

rain   hat   see   red

mane   map   feet   pet

cake   bag   bean   bed

a b c d e f g h i j k l m n o p q r s t u v w x y z

■ Trace the path from the arrow (➡) to the star (★) by connecting words with the long "a" sound. (Say) each word as you go.

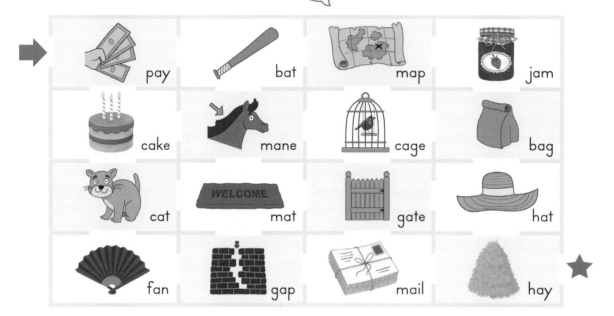

■ Trace the path from the arrow (➡) to the star (★) by connecting words with the long "e" sound. (Say) each word as you go.

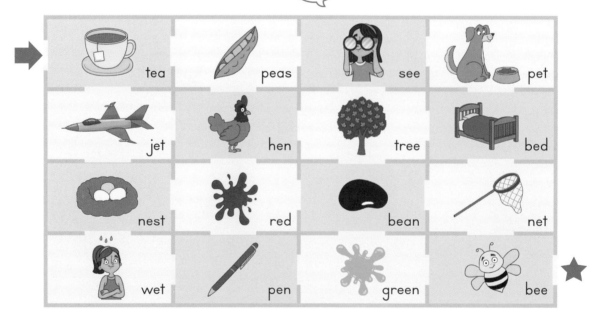

a b c d e f g h i j k l m n o p q r s t u v w x y z

Long Vowel Sounds

Comparing Long and Short "i" and "o"

Name

Date

/ /

■ Trace each path from dot (●) to star (★) by following the words with the same vowel sound. (Say) each word as you go.

long "i"   short "i"   long "o"   short "o"

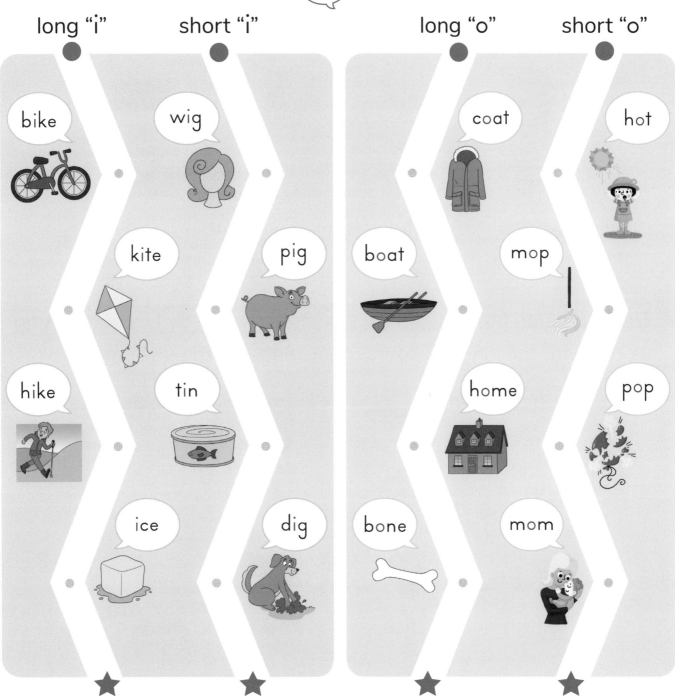

■ Trace the path from the arrow (➡) to the star (★) by connecting words with the long "i" sound. (Say) each word as you go.

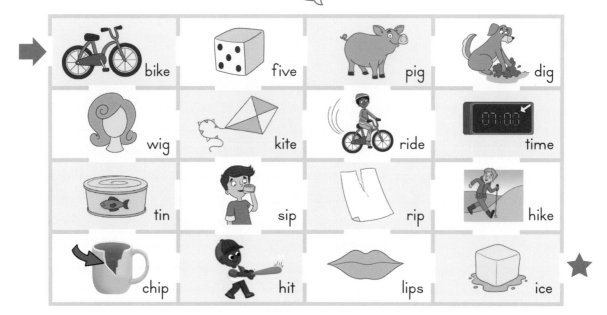

■ Trace the path from the arrow (➡) to the star (★) by connecting words with the long "o" sound. (Say) each word as you go.

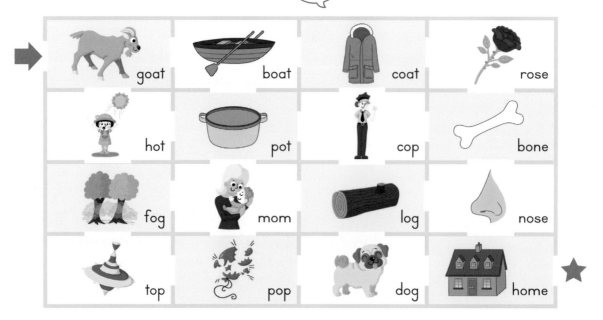

| a | b | c | d | e | f | g | h | i | j | k | l | m | n | o | p | q | r | s | t | u | v | w | x | y | z |

Long Vowel Sounds

Long and Short "u" / "y" as a Vowel

Name

Date

/ /

To parents/guardians: This section will review long and short vowel sounds. You will notice that the second puzzle reviews y as a vowel. Remind your child that y as a vowel can make the long "i" or long "e" sound.

■ Trace each path from dot (●) to star (★) by following the words with the same vowel sound. (Say) each word as you go.

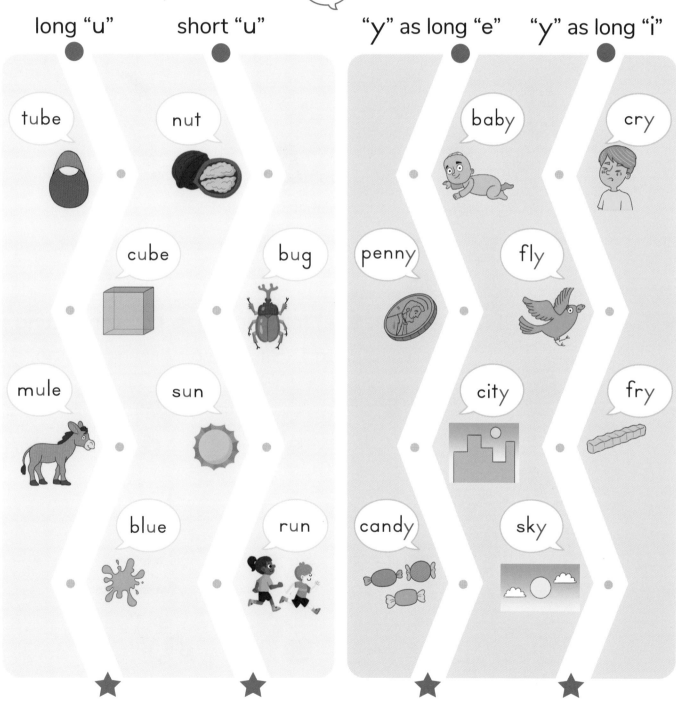

long "u"   short "u"   "y" as long "e"   "y" as long "i"

tube   nut   baby   cry

cube   bug   penny   fly

mule   sun   city   fry

blue   run   candy   sky

a b c d e f g h i j k l m n o p q r s t u v w x y z

- Trace the path from the arrow (➡) to the star (★) by connecting words with the long "u" sound. (Say) each word as you go.

- Trace the path from the arrow (➡) to the star (★) by connecting words with the "y" as long "i" sound. (Say) each word as you go.

| a | b | c | d | e | f | g | h | i | j | k | l | m | n | o | p | q | r | s | t | u | v | w | x | y | z |

26 Consonant Combinations
The "bl" Blend

Name

Date

/   /

To parents/guardians: This page begins the section on consonant blends. Have your child practice saying the words out loud to better hear the blend sounds.

■ (Say) the word represented by the picture out loud. Then circle the letters that make the "bl" sound.

b l u e

b l o c k

b l a c k

b l o w

b l o o m

b l i m p

b l a n k e t

b l o n d

| a | b | c | d | e | f | g | h | i | j | k | l | m | n | o | p | q | r | s | t | u | v | w | x | y | z |

51

To parents/guardians: The activity on this page will help your child break down the sound of the consonant blend into two sounds they already know.

■ (Say) the word represented by the picture out loud. Then write in the missing letter(s).

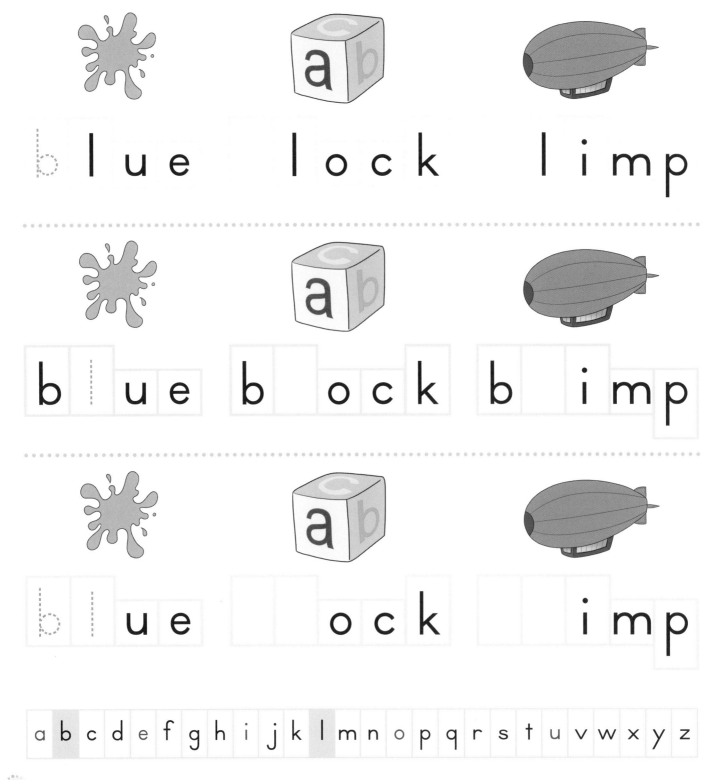

b l u e   l o c k   l i m p

b l u e   b o c k   b i m p

b l u e   o c k   i m p

a b c d e f g h i j k l m n o p q r s t u v w x y z

Consonant Combinations

The "cl" Blend

■ (Say) the word represented by the picture out loud. Then circle the letters that make the "cl" sound.

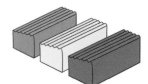

c l e a n   c l a m   c l a y

c l a p   c l a w   c l o u d

c l u e   c l o c k

a b c d e f g h i j k l m n o p q r s t u v w x y z

■ (Say) the word represented by the picture out loud. Then write in the missing letter(s).

c l o c k   l o u d   l a w

c l o c k   c _ o u d   c _ a w

c l o c k   _ o u d   _ a w

a b c d e f g h i j k l m n o p q r s t u v w x y z

Consonant Combinations
The "fl" Blend

■ (Say) the word represented by the picture out loud. Then circle the letters that make the "fl" sound.

f l a g

f l o a t

f l a m e

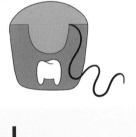

f l o s s

f l o o r

f l y

f l o w e r

f l u f f y

a b c d e f g h i j k l m n o p q r s t u v w x y z

■ (Say) the word represented by the picture out loud. Then write in the missing letter(s).

f l a g   l o s s   l a m e

f l a g   f o s s   f a m e

f l a g   o s s   a m e

a b c d e f g h i j k l m n o p q r s t u v w x y z

Consonant Combinations

The "gl" Blend

■ (Say) the word represented by the picture out loud. Then circle the letters that make the "gl" sound.

g l o w   g l a d   g l o v e s

g l u e   g l a s s   g l o b e

g l i t t e r   g l a s s e s

a b c d e f g h i j k l m n o p q r s t u v w x y z

■ (Say) the word represented by the picture out loud. Then write in the missing letter(s).

g l u e   l o b e   l o v e s

g l u e   g o b e   g o v e s

g l u e   o b e   o v e s

a b c d e f g h i j k l m n o p q r s t u v w x y z

30 Consonant Combinations
Reviewing "bl", "cl", "fl", and "gl"

Name

Date

/   /

To parents/guardians: Here your child will review consonant combinations from the previous pages. If your child has difficulty, point out that there are two words in each row that contain the letter blend.

■ Say the words in each row out loud. Two words in each row have the letter blend shown. Circle them.

■ Trace each path from dot (●) to star (★) by following the words that begin with the same letter blend sound. (Say) each word as you go.

Consonant Combinations
The "br" Blend

■ (Say) the word represented by the picture out loud. Then circle the letters that make the "br" sound.

b(r)own

brick

brush

bridge

braid

bread

broken

brother

a b c d e f g h i j k l m n o p q r s t u v w x y z

■ (Say) the word represented by the picture out loud. Then write in the missing letter(s).

b r e a d   r i c k   r u s h

b r e a d   b i c k   b u s h

b r e a d   i c k   u s h

a b c d e f g h i j k l m n o p q r s t u v w x y z

32 Consonant Combinations

The "cr" Blend

■ (Say) the word represented by the picture out loud. Then circle the letters that make the "cr" sound.

(c r) y

c r a t e

c r a w l

c r a b

c r o w n

c r a c k

c r a y o n

c r a n e

| a | b | c | d | e | f | g | h | i | j | k | l | m | n | o | p | q | r | s | t | u | v | w | x | y | z |

■ (Say) the word represented by the picture out loud. Then write in the missing letter(s).

c r y   r a n e   r o w n

c r y   c a n e   c o w n

c r y   a n e   o w n

a b c d e f g h i j k l m n o p q r s t u v w x y z

Consonant Combinations

The "fr" Blend

■ Say the word represented by the picture out loud. Then circle the letters that make the "fr" sound.

frog

fruit

frown

fry

free

frame

friend

freeze

a b c d e f g h i j k l m n o p q r s t u v w x y z

- ■ (Say) the word represented by the picture out loud. Then write in the missing letter(s).

f r o g   r u i t   r y

f r o g   f u i t   f y

f r o g   u i t   y

a b c d e f g h i j k l m n o p q r s t u v w x y z

34 Consonant Combinations
The "gr" Blend

Date
/ /

■ (Say) the word represented by the picture out loud. Then circle the letters that make the "gr" sound.

g r a s s

g r o u p

g r o w

g r e e n

g r i l l

g r a y

g r a p h

g r a p e s

a b c d e f g h i j k l m n o p q r s t u v w x y z

■ (Say) the word represented by the picture out loud. Then write in the missing letter(s).

g r e e n   r i l l   r o w

g r e e n   g i l l   g ow

g r e e n   i l l   ow

a b c d e f g h i j k l m n o p q r s t u v w x y z

35 Consonant Combinations

Reviewing "br", "cr", "fr", and "gr"

To parents/guardians: Here your child will review consonant combinations from the previous pages. Make sure your child says each word represented by the picture out loud, so they can correctly circle the words that begin with each letter blend.

■ (Say) the words in each row out loud. Two words in each row have the letter blend shown. Circle them.

| a | b | c | d | e | f | g | h | i | j | k | l | m | n | o | p | q | r | s | t | u | v | w | x | y | z |

■ Trace each path from dot (●) to star (★) by following the words that begin with the same letter blend sound. (Say) each word as you go.

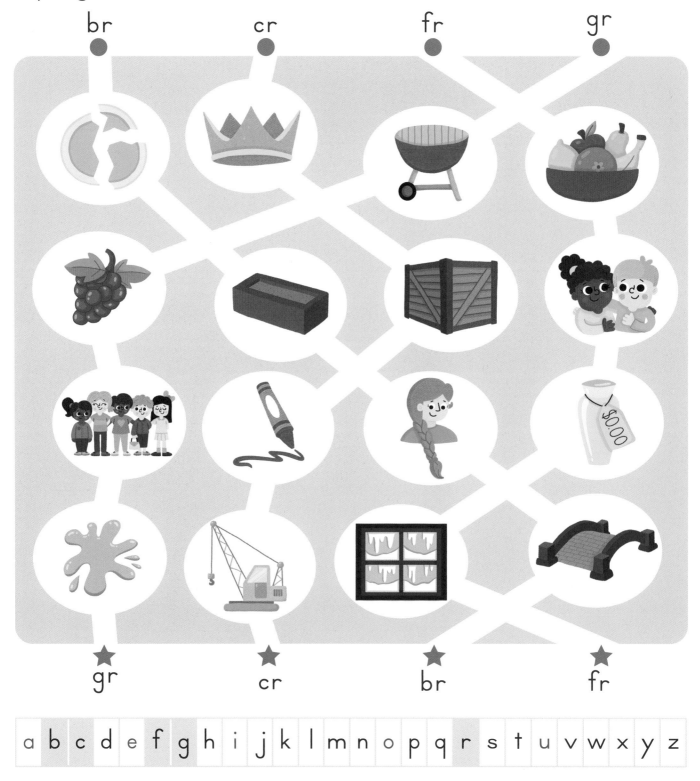

■ (Say) the word represented by the picture out loud. Then circle the letters that make the "tr" sound.

t r e e

tray

truck

trap

train

trunk

trail

trash

a b c d e f g h i j k l m n o p q r s t u v w x y z

■ (Say) the word represented by the picture out loud. Then write in the missing letter(s).

t r a y   r u c k   r a i n

t r a y   t u c k   t a i n

t r a y   _ u c k   _ a i n

a b c d e f g h i j k l m n o p q r s t u v w x y z

37

Consonant Combinations

The "dr" Blend

■ (Say) the word represented by the picture out loud. Then circle the letters that make the "dr" sound.

dry

drop

drill

dress

drum

drink

dragon

dream

a b c d e f g h i j k l m n o p q r s t u v w x y z

■ (Say) the word represented by the picture out loud. Then write in the missing letter(s).

d r e s s   r u m   r i n k

d r e s s   d um   d ink

d r e s s   um   ink

a b c d e f g h i j k l m n o p q r s t u v w x y z

38

Consonant Combinations

The "sl" Blend

■ (Say) the word represented by the picture out loud. Then circle the letters that make the "sl" sound.

s l i p

s l u g

s l e e p

s l i d e

s l e d

s l o t h

s l e e v e

s l i p p e r

a	b	c	d	e	f	g	h	i	j	k	l	m	n	o	p	q	r	s	t	u	v	w	x	y	z

■ (Say) the word represented by the picture out loud. Then write in
the missing letter(s).

s l e d   l u g   l o t h

s   e d   s   u g   s   o t h

s   e d   u g   o t h

a b c d e f g h i j k l m n o p q r s t u v w x y z

39

Consonant Combinations

The "pl" Blend

Name _____

Date _____ / _____ / _____

■ (Say) the word represented by the picture out loud. Then circle the letters that make the "pl" sound.

p l a y

p l o w

p l a n t

p l a t e

p l u m

p l u g

p l a n e t

p l a n e

a b c d e f g h i j k l m n o p q r s t u v w x y z

■ (Say) the word represented by the picture out loud. Then write in the missing letter(s).

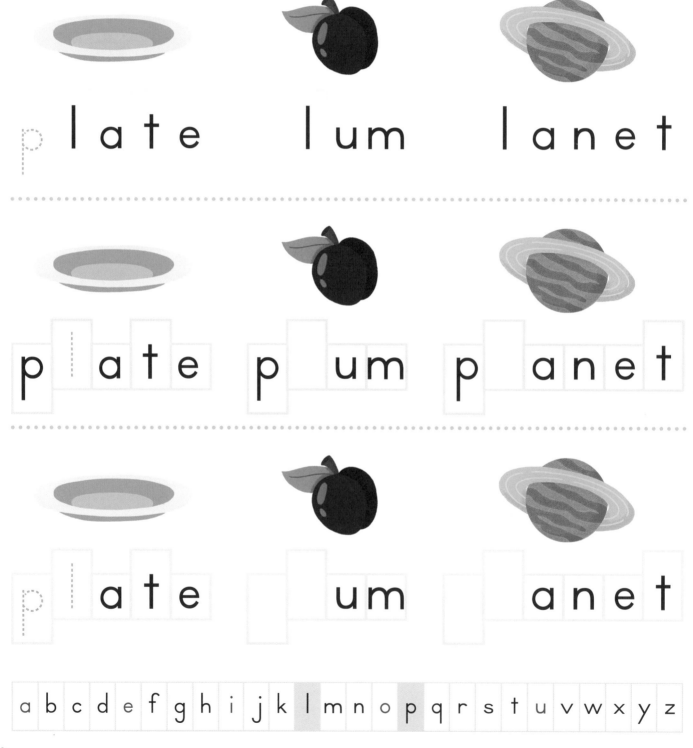

p l a t e   l u m   l a n e t

p l a t e   p u m   p a n e t

p l a t e   u m   a n e t

a b c d e f g h i j k l m n o p q r s t u v w x y z

40

Consonant Combinations

Reviewing "tr", "dr", "sl", and "pl"

Name

Date

/ /

■ (Say) the words in each row out loud. Two words in each row have the letter blend shown. Circle them.

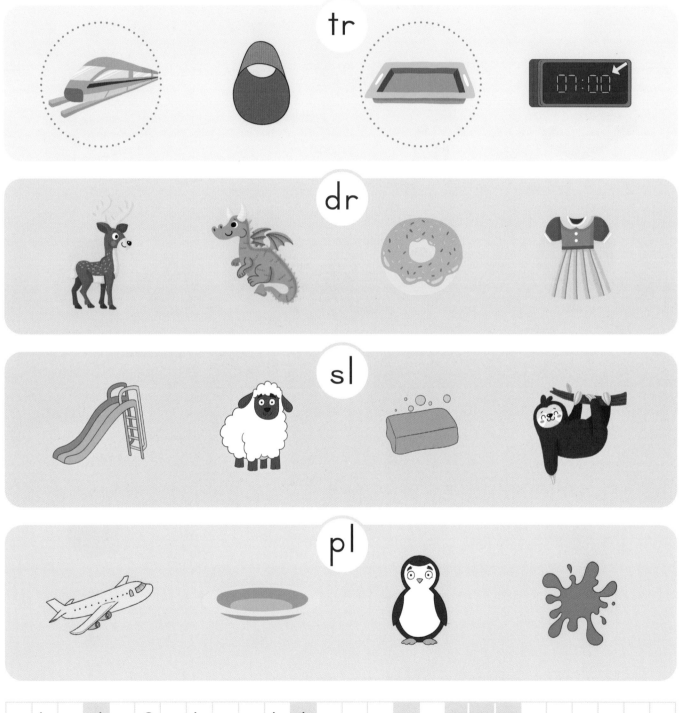

a b c d e f g h i j k l m n o p q r s t u v w x y z

■ Trace each path from dot (●) to star (★) by following the words that begin with the same letter blend sound. (Say) each word as you go.

Consonant Combinations
The "ch" Digraph

Name

Date

/   /

To parents/guardians: This page begins the section on consonant digraphs. Digraphs are letter combinations in which the two letters make one new sound. It is important for your child to say each word out loud several times to better identify the digraph sound.

■ (Say) the word represented by the picture out loud. Then circle the letters that make the "ch" sound.

chip

chop

cherry

chair

chick

chin

cheese

check

a b c d e f g h i j k l m n o p q r s t u v w x y z

■ Draw a line along the path from the dot (●) to the star (★).
Each time you pass an image, (say) the word out loud.

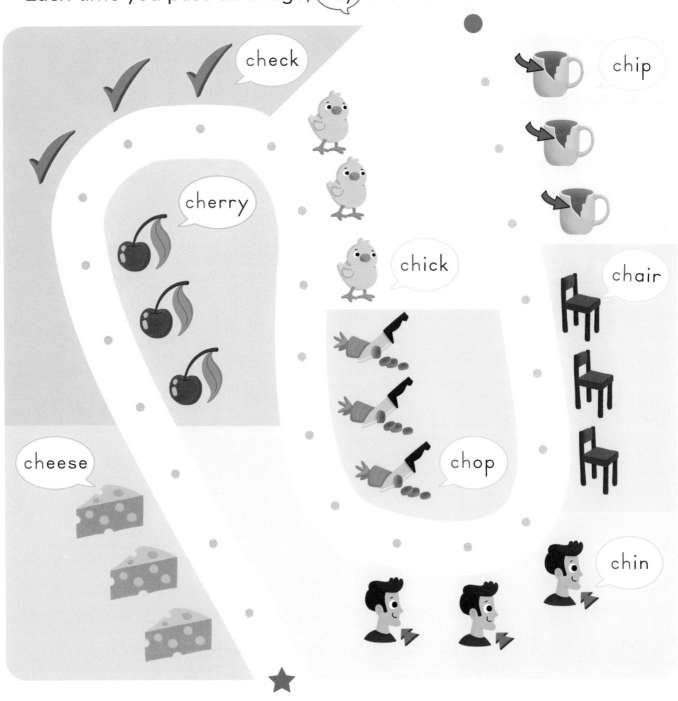

a b c d e f g h i j k l m n o p q r s t u v w x y z

42 Consonant Combinations
The "sh" Digraph

■ (Say) the word represented by the picture out loud. Then circle the letters that make the "sh" sound.

(s h)e e p

s h i r t

s h o e

s h a r k

s h e l l

s h i p

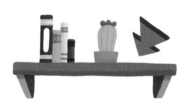

s h e l f

s h a d o w

| a | b | c | d | e | f | g | h | i | j | k | l | m | n | o | p | q | r | s | t | u | v | w | x | y | z |

■ Draw a line along the path from the dot (●) to the star (★).
Each time you pass an image, (say) the word out loud.

43 Consonant Combinations
The "th" Digraph

Name

Date / /

To parents/guardians: The words in the last row of this page introduce the idea that a consonant digraph can appear at the end of a word, as well as at the beginning. If your child is confused by this, you can offer them help by saying something like, "The 'th' in 'throw' sounds like the 'th' in 'bath.' Can you hear it?"

■ (Say) the word represented by the picture out loud. Then circle the letters that make the "th" sound.

(t)hink   three   throw

thirsty   thorn

ba(th)   moth   mouth

a b c d e f g h i j k l m n o p q r s t u v w x y z

Draw a line along the path from the dot (●) to the star (★).
Each time you pass an image, say the word out loud.

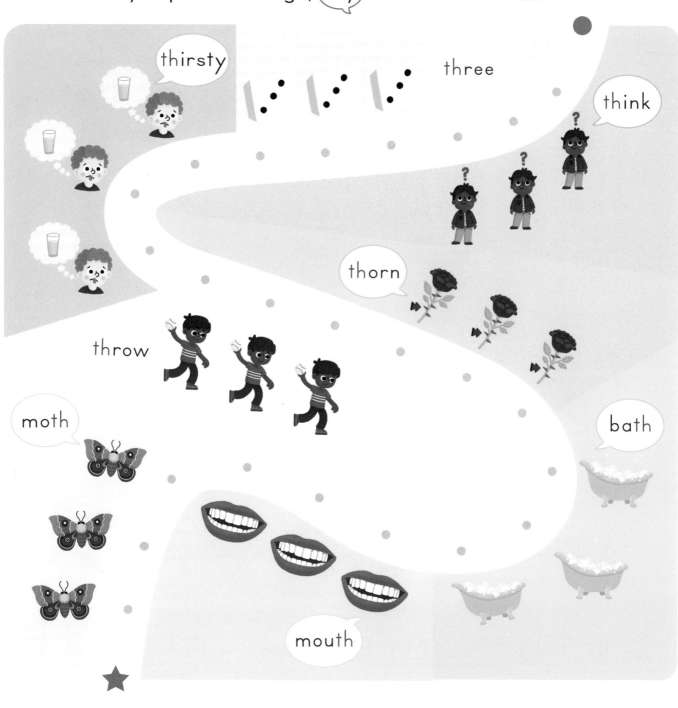

a b c d e f g h i j k l m n o p q r s t u v w x y z

44 Consonant Combinations

Reviewing "ch", "sh", and "th"

Name

Date

/   /

To parents/guardians: Here your child will review digraphs. It is important to have your child say each word out loud as they complete the activity. This will help them associate each letter combination with the sound it makes.

■ (Say) the words in each row out loud. Two words in each row have the letter blend shown. Circle them.

a b c d e f g h i j k l m n o p q r s t u v w x y z

■ Trace each path from dot (●) to star (★) by following the words that begin with the same letter blend sound. (Say) each word as you go.

45 Consonant Combinations Review

Blends and Digraphs

Name

Date

/ /

To parents/guardians: This is the final section in this book. If your child has completed all the activities, please give them a lot of praise. You can also present your child with the Certificate of Achievement on the final page of this book.

■ ⬤Say⬤ the word represented by the picture out loud. Then circle the letters that make the beginning sound of the word.

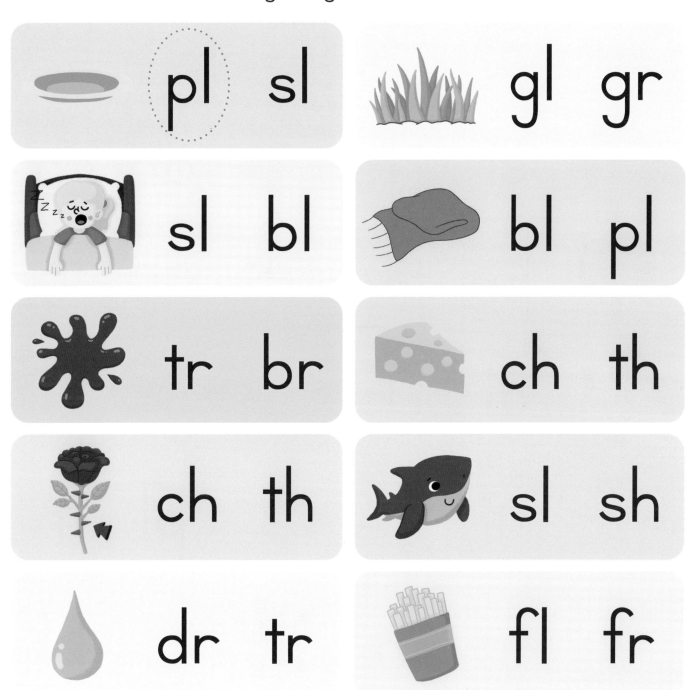

■ (Say) the word represented by the picture out loud. Then circle the letters that make the beginning sound of the word.

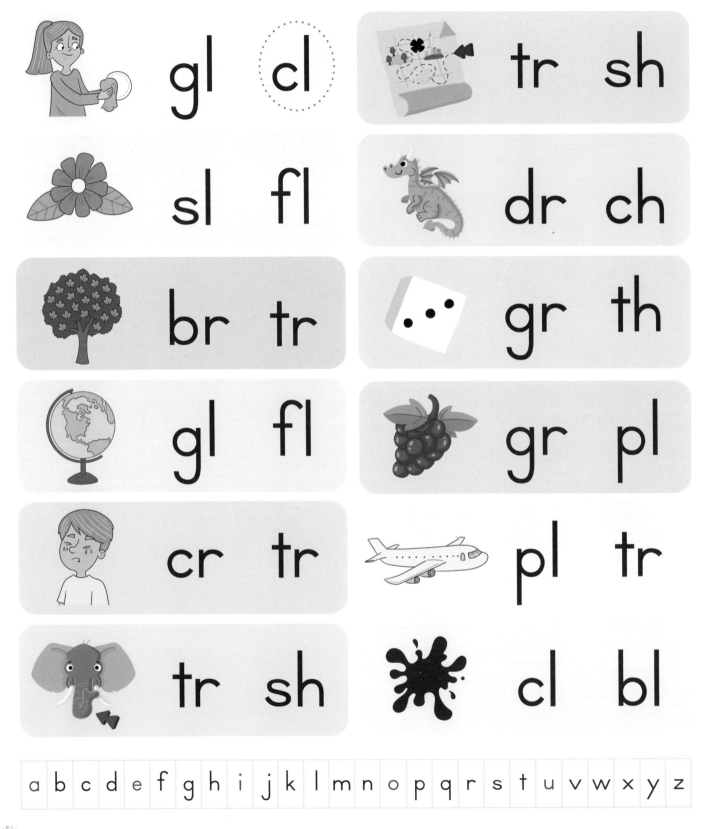

gl　(cl)

tr　sh

sl　fl

dr　ch

br　tr

gr　th

gl　fl

gr　pl

cr　tr

pl　tr

tr　sh

cl　bl

a	b	c	d	e	f	g	h	i	j	k	l	m	n	o	p	q	r	s	t	u	v	w	x	y	z

My Book of Reading Skills: Phonics Answer Key

page 1

page 2

page 3

page 4

page 5

page 6

page 7

page 8

page 9

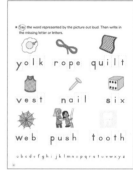

page 10

page 11

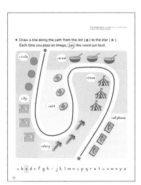

page 12

page 13

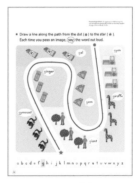

page 14

page 15

page 16

page 17

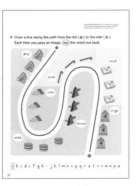

page 18

page 19

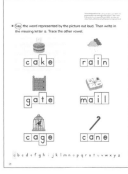

page 20

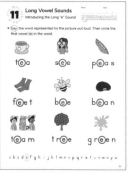

page 21

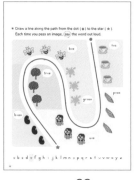

page 22

page 23

page 24

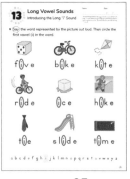

page 25

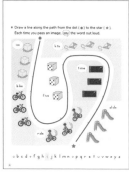

page 26

page 27

page 28

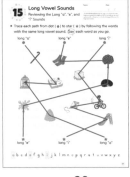

page 29

page 30

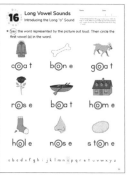

page 31

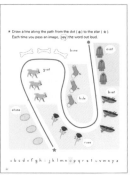

page 32

page 33

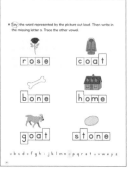

page 34

page 35

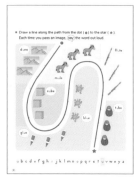

page 36

page 37

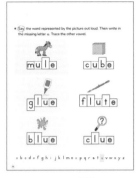

page 38

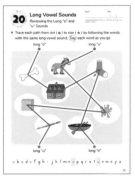

page 39

page 40

page 41

page 42

page 43

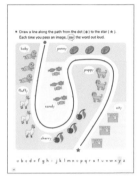

page 44

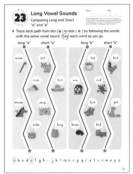

page 45

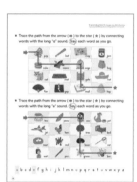

page 46

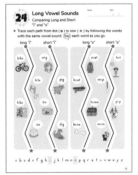

page 47

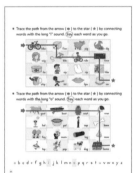

page 48

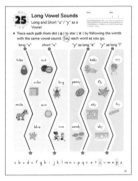

page 49

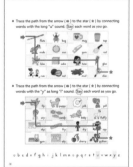

page 50

page 51

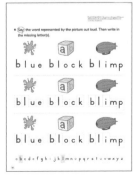

page 52

page 53

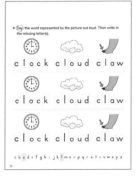

page 54

My Book of Reading Skills: Phonics Answer Key

page 55

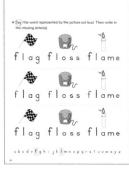

page 56

page 57

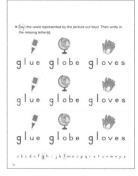

page 58

page 59

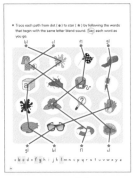

page 60

page 61

page 62

page 63

page 64

page 65

page 66

page 67

page 68

page 69

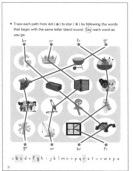

page 70

page 71

page 72

My Book of Reading Skills: Phonics Answer Key

page 73

page 74

page 75

page 76

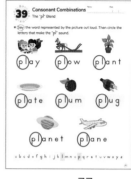

page 77

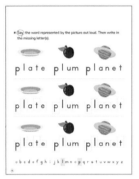

page 78

page 79

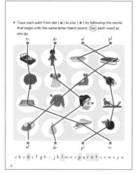

page 80

page 81

page 82

page 83

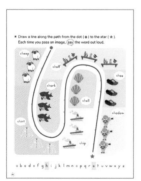

page 84

page 85

page 86

page 87

page 88

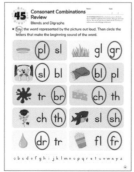

page 89

page 90

Certificate of Achievement

is hereby congratulated on completing

My Book of Reading Skills: Phonics

Presented on

, 20

Parent or guardian

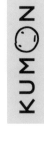

KUM◯N